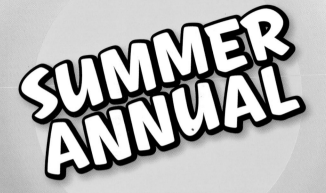

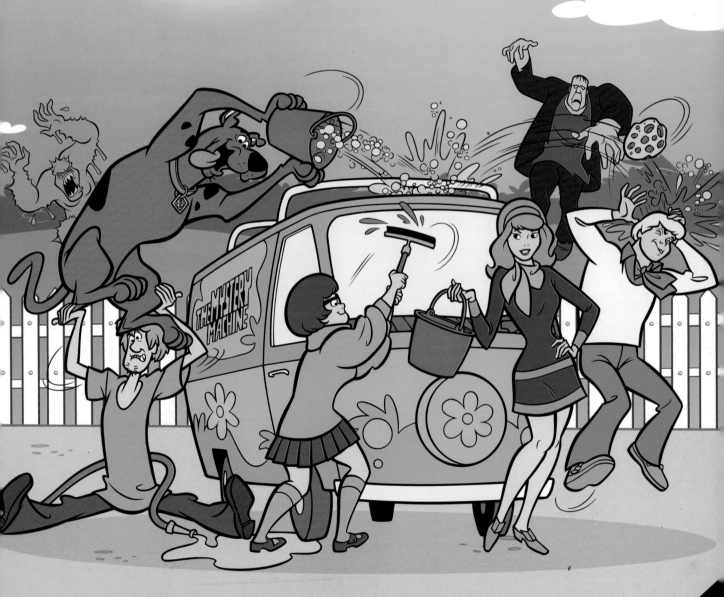

£7.99

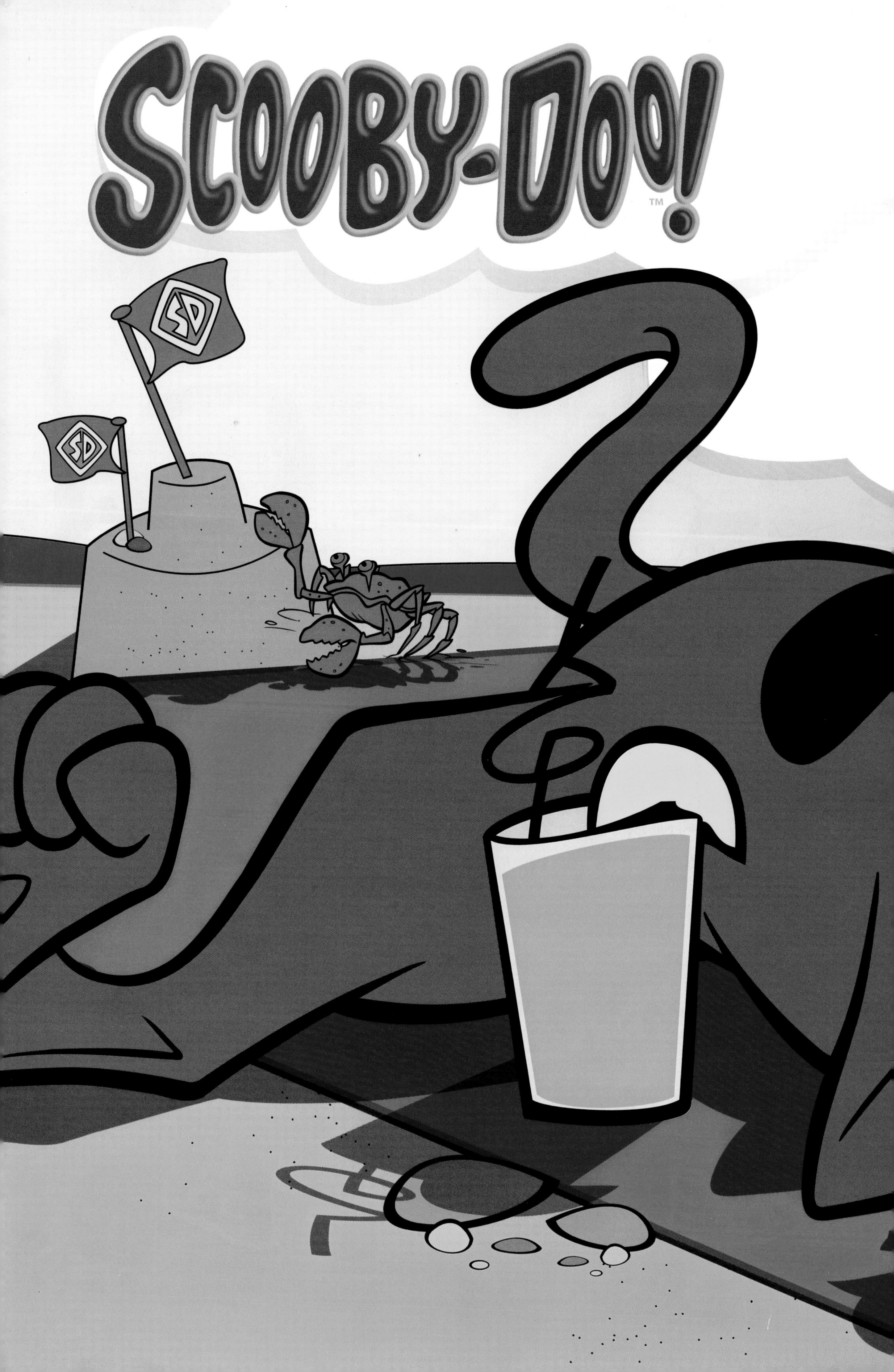
SCOOBY-DOO!™

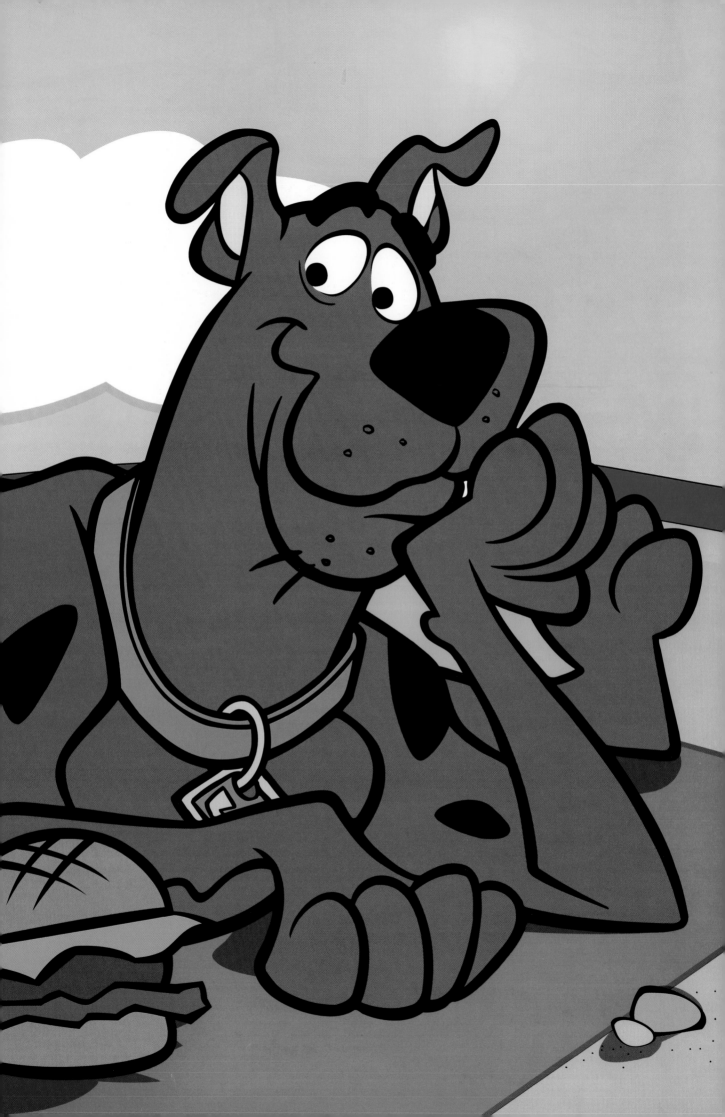

WELCOME

THIS ANNUAL BELONGS TO...

MINI MYSTERY

There are 10 bottles of sun cream hidden within the Annual. Help the gang to find them before they get sun burnt and list the page numbers below!

Answers on page 63

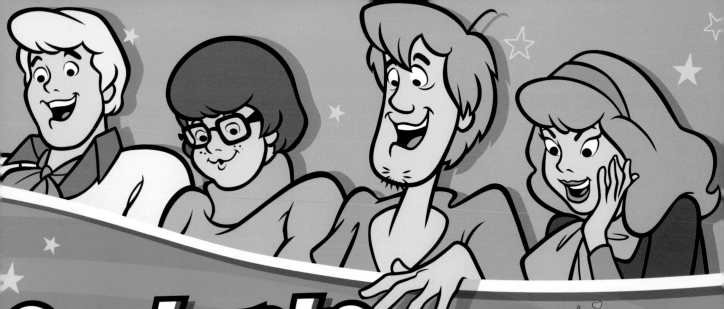

Contents

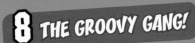

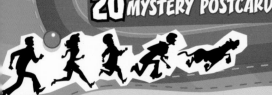
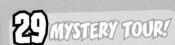
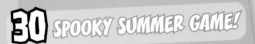
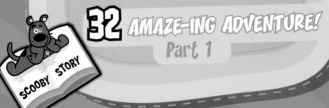
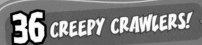

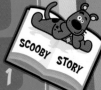
SD MAKE

THE GROOVY GANG

Scooby

NAME: Scoobert-Doo

FAVE COLOUR: Brown

GREATEST FEAR: Ghosts, especially Screaming Banshees

FAVE DAY TRIP: Visiting Velma's Aunty Zelma cos she makes the best banana cookies ever!

YUMMIEST SANDWICH: A tuna and sweetcorn sub with Scooby Snacks sprinkled on top!

BEST DAY: Christmas, cos of all the treats!

SCOOBY SECRET: He's really ticklish!

Shaggy

NAME: Norville Rogers

FAVE COLOUR: Green

BEST PLACE IN THE WORLD: The gang's favourite hang-out, The Malt Shop

AMBITION: To own a Scooby Snacks factory, mm-mmm!

FAVE ACCESSORY: My lucky roller skates, cos no ghoul can ever catch me when I'm wearing them!

WORST THING EVER: Being called Norville!

FAVE CAKE: Lemon drizzle cup cakes with a cherry on top!

Velma

NAME: Velma Dinkley

FAVE COLOUR: Orange

FUNNIEST MEMORY: When Shaggy and Scooby dressed up as a pantomime cow to hide from a ghost!

FAVE PASTA DISH: Macaroni cheese

WORST FEAR: Losing my glasses

NO. 1 HERO: Sherlock Holmes

Daphne

NAME: Daphne Blake

FAVE COLOUR: Purple

FAVE FLOWER: Daisy

BESTEST DAY OUT: Hitting the shops and then a trip to the cinema!

WORST EXPERIENCE: Doing a home perm kit - curly hair is soo not me!

FAVE SWEET TREAT: Chocolate Ice Cream

Fred

NAME: Fred Jones

FAVE COLOUR: Blue

BEST FEATURE: My teeth

WORST DESSERT: Rice pudding

FAVE SUPERHERO: Spider-Man

PROUDEST MOMENT: Appearing in Monster-Catcher magazine as Man of the Month

GOAL: To solve the mystery of the Loch Ness Monster

I'M GLAD YOU COULD MAKE IT OUT HERE TO *HAWAII*, FRED! YOU AND YOUR FRIENDS CAN HELP ME DESIGN A *FAMILY* HOTEL ON THIS BEACH-FRONT I BOUGHT.

IT'S THE LEAST I COULD DO FOR AN OLD FAMILY FRIEND, WALTER!

I'D BE GLAD TO CHECK IN ANYTIME! THIS AREA OF THE BEACH IS SPECTACULAR!

OF COURSE, A LOT WILL DEPEND ON THE ANGLE AND COMPOSITION OF THE WAVES TOMORROW. WITH GREAT WAVES, YOU'LL HAVE A GREAT RESORT!

LIKE, WITH LUAUS LIKE THIS, YOU CAN'T MISS! PASS THE *POI*, SCOOB!

REAH! RUM-*MY!*

IN ADDITION TO GREAT FOOD AND GREAT SURFING, WE'LL ALSO BE OFFERING ALL SORTS OF AUTHENTIC HAWAIIAN ENTERTAINMENT!

LIKE THE AREA'S STORYTELLER-- AND HERE HE IS NOW!

YOU ARE A BRAVE *KANAKA**...

* *Outsider in Hawaiian*

SURF'S UP, MONSTER'S DOWN

...OR DON'T YOU KNOW THIS BEACH IS *HAUNTED*?!

RAUNTED?

LIKE, I LOST MY APPETITE!

writer: PAUL S. NEWMAN pencils: DON PERLIN
inks: DAN DAVIS letters: JOHN COSTANZA
colors: PAUL BECTON assists: HARVEY RICHARDS
edits: DANA KURTIN

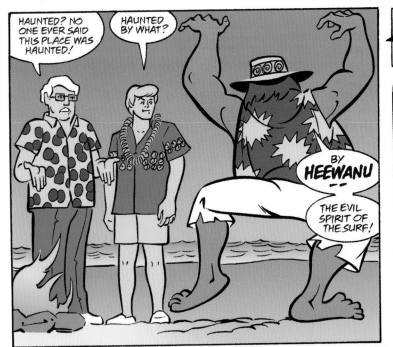

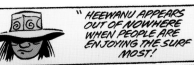

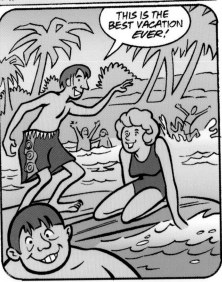

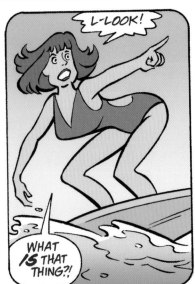

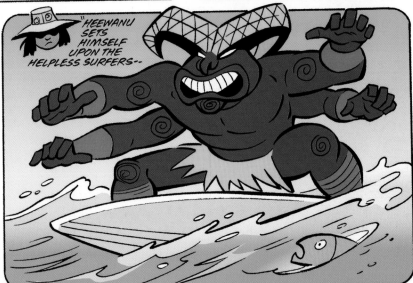

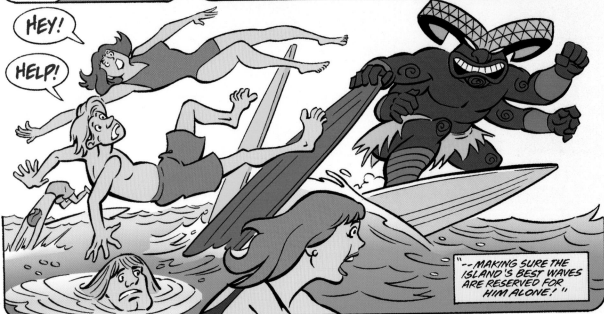

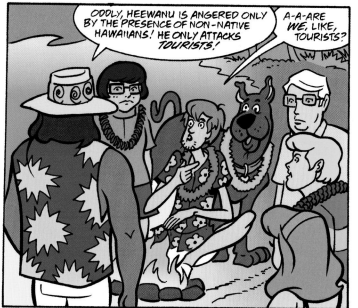

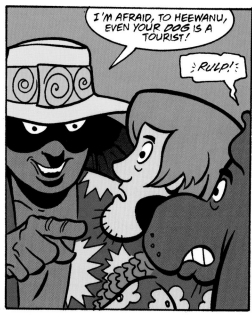

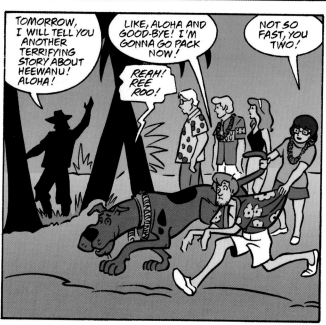

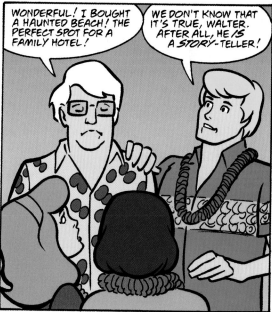

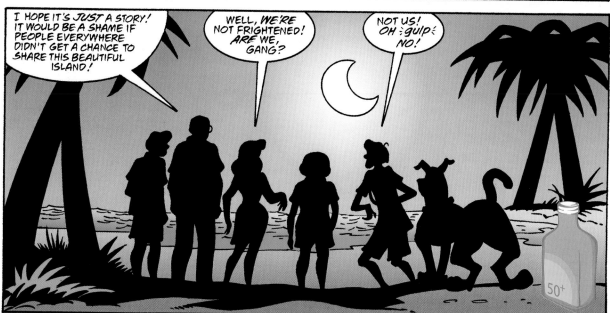

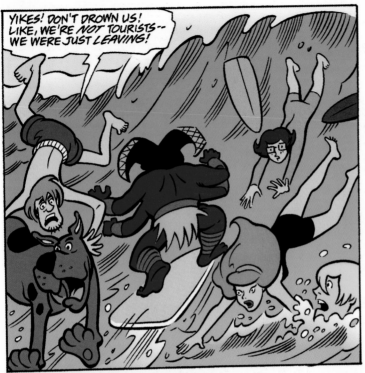

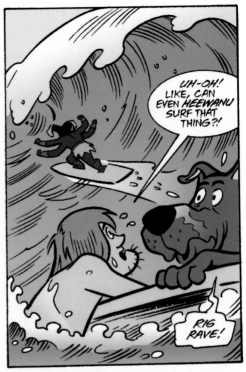

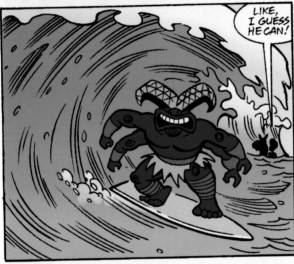

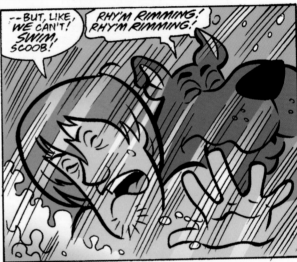

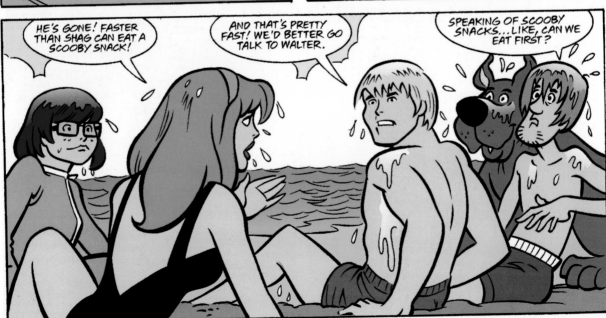

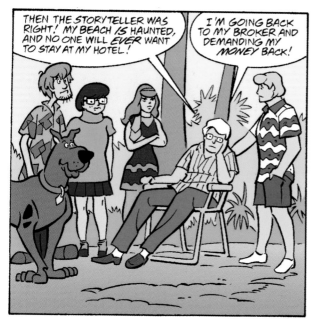

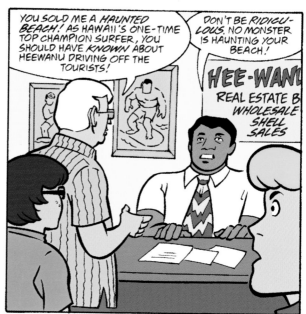

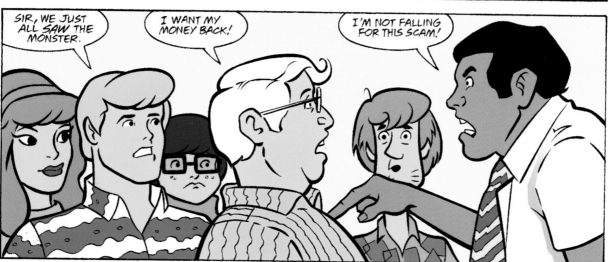

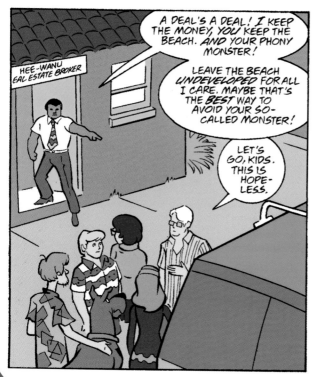

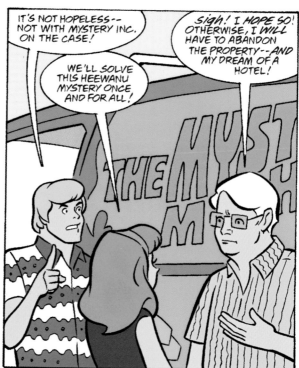

CONTINUED ON PAGE 16

WAVE CRAZE!

Scooby-Doo is riding the waves like a pro! Can you copy the scene into the grid below before he falls off his surf board? When you have finished, colour him in!

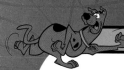

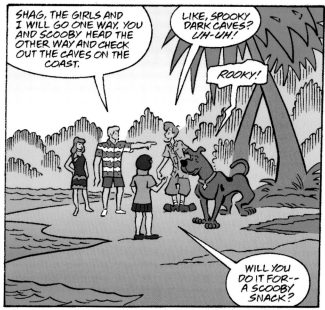

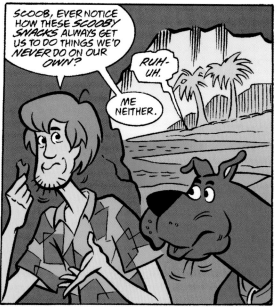

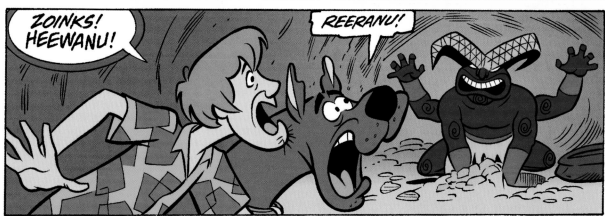

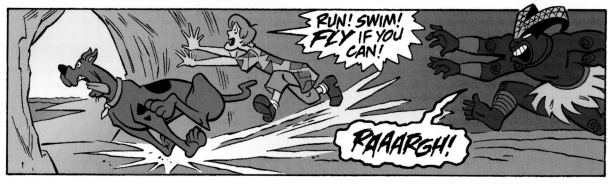

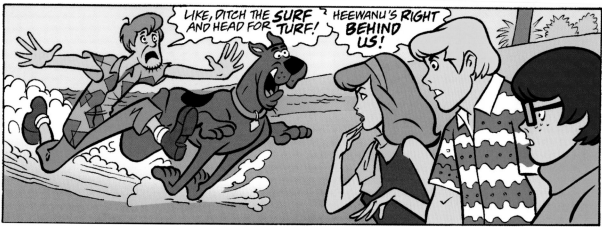

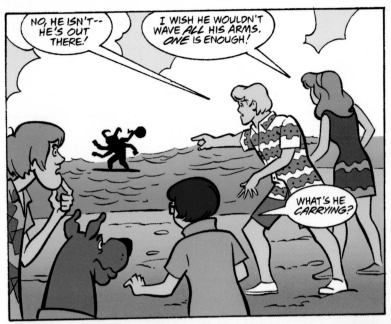

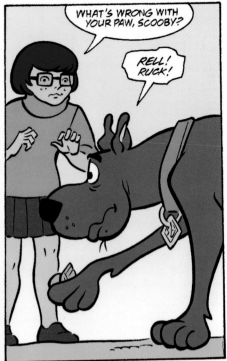

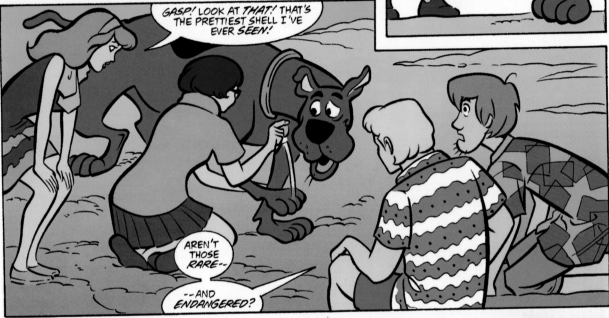

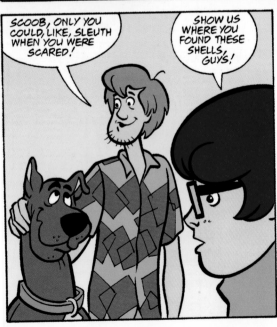

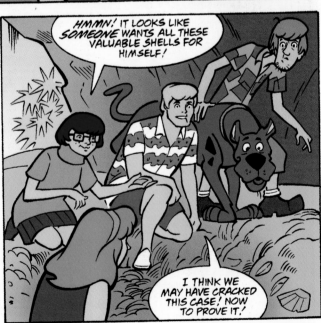

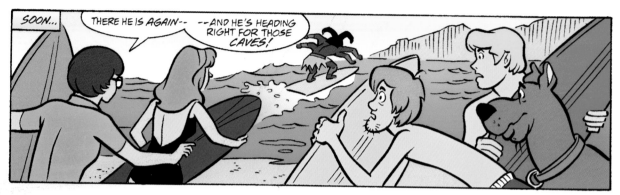

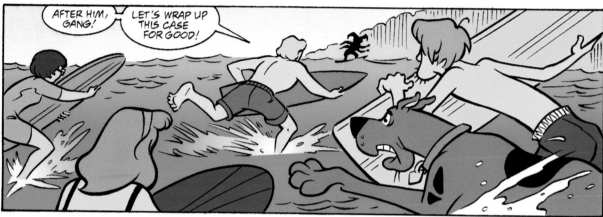

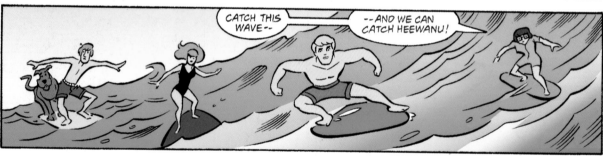

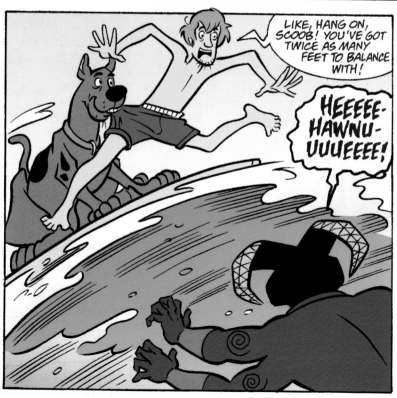

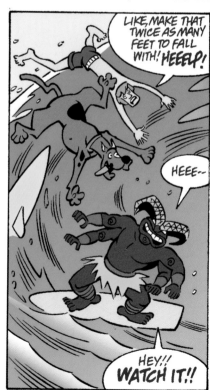

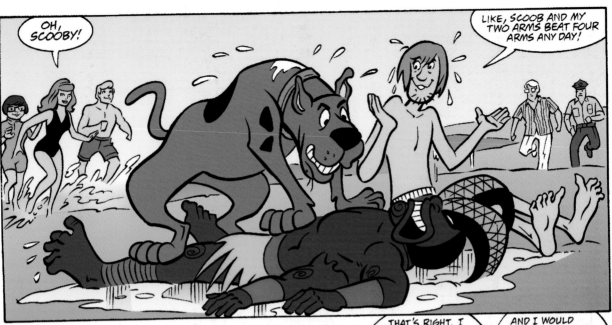

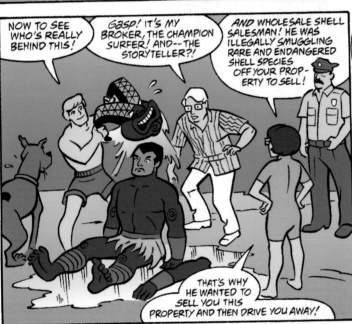

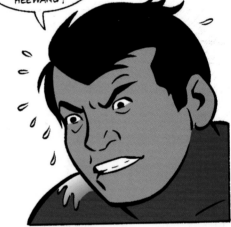

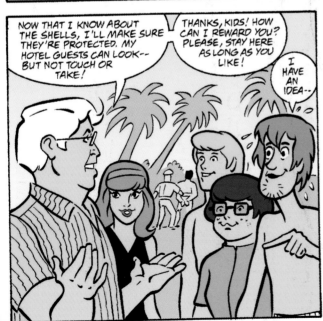

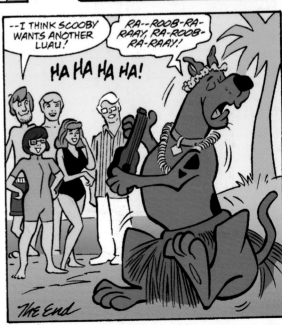

MYSTERY POSTCARDS!

The gang have been on their summer holidays and have each sent a postcard. Check out each one and discover what they have been up to!

★ Velma ★

Hi everyone,

Having a fantastic time! The sun is shining and it's really hot here. I've seen lots of camels!

I've heard a fascinating story that there is an angry mummy on the loose. It's terrifying all the tourists. I'm looking forward to investigating!

See you soon,

Velma xx

Mystery_In
224 Maple
Coolsville

KIDS

QUESTIONS!

Where did Velma go for her holiday?

Answer:

What pointy building do mummies live in?

Answer:

What are mummies wrapped in?

Answer:

★ Fred ★

Hi gang!

I'm having a mystery-packed time here in Hawaii! I've tried surfing but it all went crazy one day when a spooky Surf Monster appeared from the waves!

The monster is really big with two heads, sharp teeth and pink furry spots. I sure could use your help solving this mystery!

Wish you were here! Freddie

SURFING 1970

Mystery, Inc.
224, Maple St
Coolsville

Draw your sketch of the Surf Monster here...

Answers: Velma's postcard - Egypt, pyramids, bandages. **Daphne's postcard** - the 5 differences are the colour of the cuffs, spots, buckle, torch, his top underneath his coat. **Scooby Scramble** - Shortbread.

Shaggy and Scooby

[H]ey dudes!

[L]ike, we are in bonny Scotland and
[we]'re having a tip-top-tastic time!

[We] visited Loch Ness yesterday but not
[to] spot Nessie - like, no way mister!
[My] Uncle Craggy runs the McRogers
[Caf]e and Scooby and I had to go check
[it] out! It's Scoobalicious!

[We]'ll see ya soon!
[Sha]ggy and Scooby

Mystery, Inc. gang
224 Maple Street
Coolsville

Scooby Scramble

Unmuddle the letters to spell out
Scooby's fave Scottish snack:

SHBRTEAORD

Grab your crayons and complete the Scottish
scene on the front of Shaggy's postcard!

Daphne

Hi gang,
Greetings from Paris! I'm having a
lovely time! I've been shopping and
visited the Eiffel Tower.
I visited a museum today and I have
found a mystery! One of these
paintings by Monsieur L'Artist is a
fake but I can't tell which one.
Can you help me out?
Thanks guys,
Daphne xxx xxx

SPECIAL DELIVERY

Mystery, Inc. gang
224 Maple Street
Coolsville

50+

Help Daphne to spot the 5
differences between these
two paintings.

la boutiqu[e]

Scooby's top 5 faves!

There are lots of things that Scooby doesn't like (bats, ghosts, soggy sandwiches) but he has lots of favourite things too! Check out Scooby's top five things that he loves!

5 Sporty Scooby!

Scooby is a high-energy hound and he loves all kinds of sports! Football, surfing and skateboarding are some of his favourite hobbies. He's even been known to try a bit of in-line skating and skiing!

4 In on the act!

Scooby is a very creative pooch! He loves drawing, singing and even acting! His acting skills have come in very handy when he goes undercover to catch a crook. He's been known to dress up as Napoleon, a waiter, a portrait painter and even one half of a cow!

3 Scooby Snooze!

Monster-mashing can be a tough job and Scooby loves nothing more than kicking back, ready for a Scooby snooze!

He has a comfy beanbag in the back of the Mystery Machine, ready for when he feels like a dog nap!

Best buds!

2

Fred, Velma and Daphne are best friends with the goofy Great Dane and he loves to spend time with them. Shaggy is even more special cos he is Scooby's owner. The groovy duo have got a lot in common, including giant appetites and a fear of all things spooky!

1 Scooby Snacking!

Food is Scooby's tip-top, number one, bestest thing ever! Pizza is a real favourite, but nothing can come close to a big box of Scooby Snacks. He loves them so much that Velma uses them to bribe Scooby into catching crooks. These lip-smacking treats are number one in Scooby's world!

22

Velma's CRIME SOLVING

JOHN ROZUM-Writer
JOE STATON-Penciller
SCOTT McRAE-Inker
NICK J. NAPOLITANO-Letterer
HEROIC AGE-Colorist
HARVEY RICHARDS-Asst Editor
JOAN HILTY-Editor

HI, I'M *VELMA* OF *MYSTERY, INC.!*

YOU WOULDN'T KNOW BY WATCHING US AT WORK, BUT THERE ARE SUBTLE WAYS TO SOLVE A MYSTERY THAT *DON'T* INVOLVE RUNNING AROUND AND WAITING FOR THE BAD GUY TO STUMBLE INTO YOUR TRAP!

TAKE THE ART OF *FINGERPRINTING,* FOR EXAMPLE.

ON THEIR FINGERTIPS, EVERY PERSON HAS A PATTERN OF *RIDGES* AND *DEPRESSIONS* UNIQUELY THEIR OWN.

LIKE SNOWFLAKES, NO TWO PERSONS' FINGERTIPS ARE EXACTLY ALIKE!

THIS MEANS THAT ANYONE CAN BE IDENTIFIED USING NOTHING MORE THAN THEIR FINGERPRINTS!

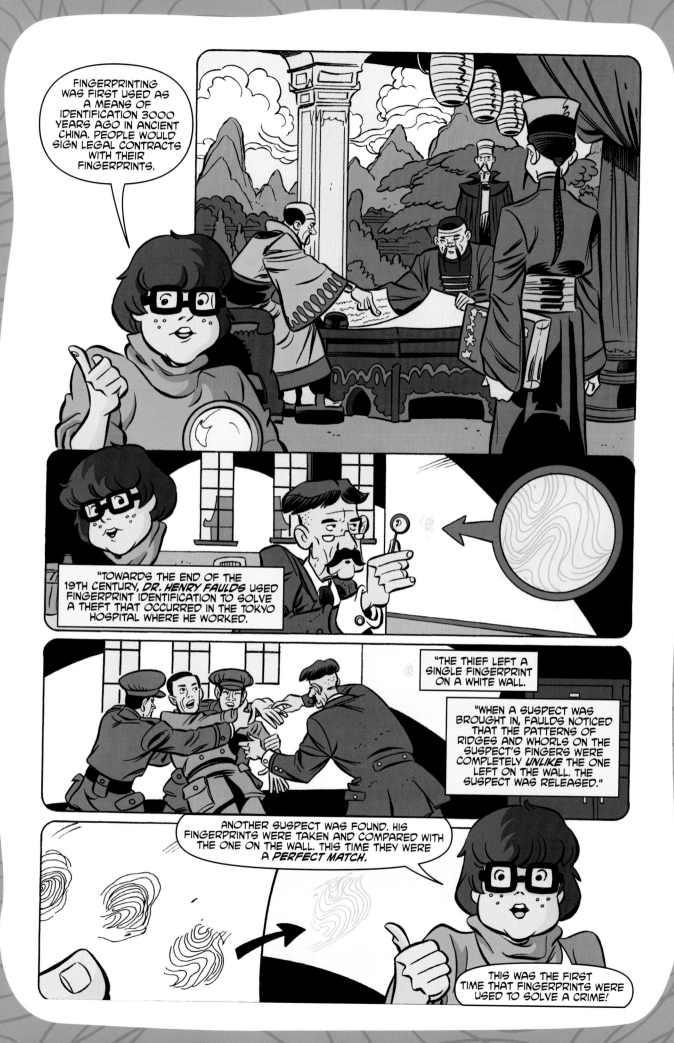

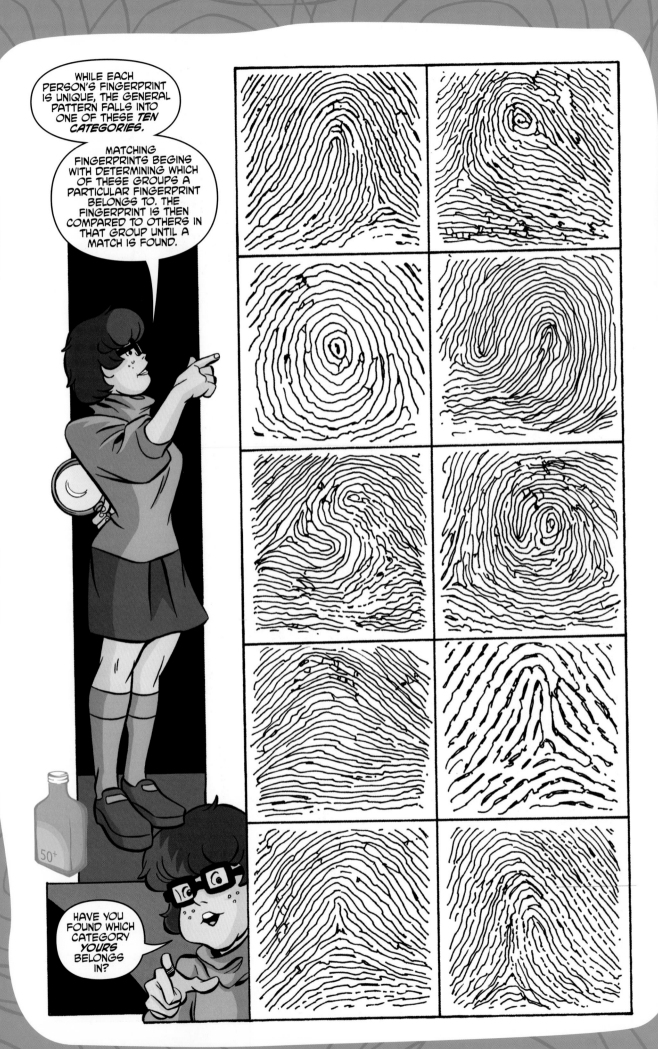

THERE ARE THREE TYPES OF FINGERPRINTS LEFT AT CRIME SCENES, SUCH AS THIS ONE.

VISIBLE PRINTS, LIKE THESE, ARE EASY TO SPOT BECAUSE THEY ARE MADE BY FINGERTIPS WHICH HAVE TOUCHED A SUBSTANCE--LIKE PAINT, INK, OR RASPBERRY JELLY.

PLASTIC PRINTS ARE MADE BY THE FINGERS PRESSED INTO A SOFT MATERIAL SUCH AS WAX, PUTTY, OR THIS BAR OF SOAP. IT'S A LOT LIKE MAKING A CAST OF THE PRINTS.

THE MOST COMMON TYPE IS ALSO THE MOST DIFFICULT TO SEE. THESE ARE *LATENT PRINTS*.

LATENT PRINTS ARE MADE WHEN THE NATURAL OILS AND SWEAT FROM A PERSON'S FINGERTIPS ARE TRANSFERRED TO A SURFACE BY TOUCHING IT. YOU CAN OFTEN SEE THESE AS "SMUDGES" ON GLASS, LIKE A WINDOWPANE, BUT IN OTHER PLACES THEY SEEM INVISIBLE.

TO SEE LATENT PRINTS, A SMOOTH SURFACE SUCH AS GLASS, PAINTED WOOD, METAL, OR TILES IS DUSTED WITH POWDER, SUCH AS THIS *DARK* CARBON POWDER USED FOR *LIGHT* SURFACES.

LIGHT-COLORED ALUMINUM POWDER IS USED ON *DARK* SURFACES. A SPECIAL FLUORESCENT POWDER IS USED ON *PATTERNED OR BRIGHTLY COLORED* SURFACES, THEN VIEWED UNDER *ULTRAVIOLET LIGHT* TO MAKE THE PRINTS STAND OUT.

THE POWDER STICKS TO THE OIL AND SWEAT LEFT BY THE FINGERTIPS. WHEN THE EXTRA POWDER IS REMOVED--

≠PHWOOOFF≠

--THE LATENT PRINT IS NOW *VISIBLE!*

ONCE A FINGERPRINT IS FOUND, IT'S IMPORTANT TO SAVE IT. THIS IS DONE BY LIFTING IT USING SHEETS OF PLASTIC, OR...

...*ADHESIVE TAPE*, WHICH ATTRACTS THE POWDER ON THE PRINT.

VRIIIIIP

GENTLY *PRESS* THE STRIP OF TAPE DOWN ONTO THE PRINT, THEN *PEEL IT AWAY*...

...LIKE *THIS*. NOW YOU CAN SEE THE PRINT HAS BEEN TRANSFERRED TO THE TAPE.

THAT'S WHY IT'S CALLED *"LIFTING* FINGERPRINTS."

THE TAPE IS THEN AFFIXED TO A WHITE CARD FOR STORAGE AND FOR FUTURE COMPARISONS.

YOU CAN EVEN TAKE FINGERPRINTS FROM PAPER AND CLOTH, LIKE THIS *TOWEL*. INSTEAD OF USING POWDERS, CHEMICALS ARE USED. MOST OFTEN, THE CLOTH IS PLACED IN A SEALED CONTAINER WITH A BIT OF GLUE.

CHEMICAL RESIDUE FROM THE GLUE'S FUMES CLINGS TO THE OILS AND SWEAT IN THE FINGERPRINT JUST LIKE THE POWDERS DO, MAKING THE PRINT VISIBLE.

BUT I DON'T THINK WE'RE GOING TO NEED ANY OF THESE TECHNIQUES TO UNCOVER WHO LEFT *THESE* PRINTS BEHIND...

27

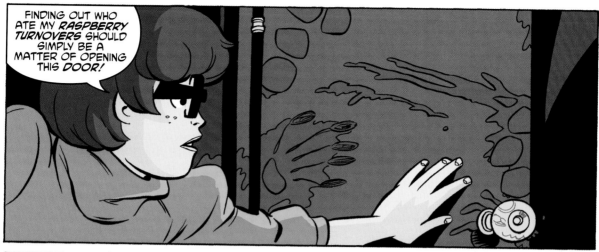

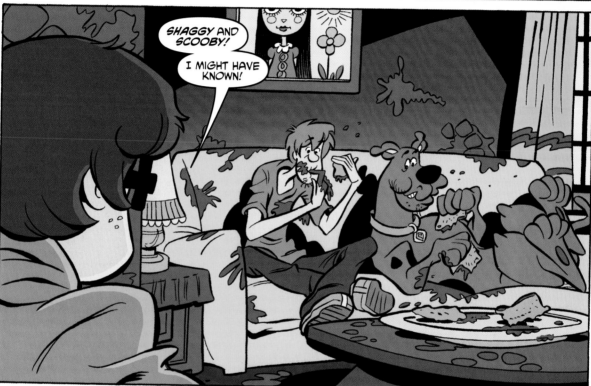

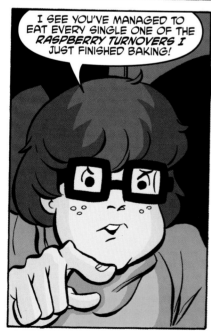

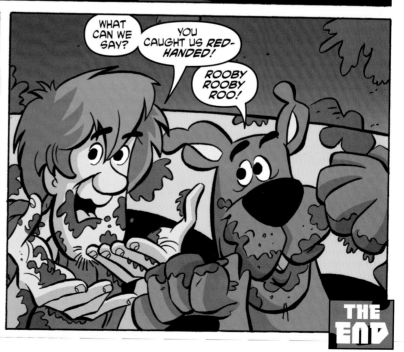

THE END

28

MYSTERY TOUR

Mystery, Inc. have travelled all over the world solving spook-packed mysteries. Can you spot all of the places they have visited in the grid?

A	X	V	O	A	S	E	L	A	W
I	H	E	A	S	C	H	I	N	A
N	A	N	L	L	Y	O	M	O	S
A	C	I	B	O	E	T	A	W	H
V	I	C	E	C	N	L	H	P	I
L	R	E	S	H	H	D	O	A	N
Y	F	I	E	N	A	V	O	E	G
S	A	N	S	E	W	A	L	N	T
N	G	O	G	S	A	N	W	H	O
A	N	Y	E	S	I	R	A	P	N
R	P	L	L	O	I	G	E	N	I
T	G	E	I	M	E	X	I	C	O

Egypt ☐　　China ☐
Peru ☐　　Paris ☐
Loch Ness ☐
Transylvania ☐　Africa ☐
Mexico ☐　London ☐
Hawaii ☐　Venice ☐
Washington ☐　Wales ☐

There is one place missing from the grid, can you work out which one it is?

....

29

Answer: Peru

YOUR MISSION!

Grab your pals and get ready to play this fun game. Spin the spinner and whoever gets the highest score goes first. Travel around the board and the first one to hit the beach wins. Beware of Giggling Green Ghosts, if you land on one you have to go back to the start! Use the spinner and counters below to play the game.

Trace the spinner and playing pieces and stick them to a piece of thin card. Push a pencil through the centre of the spinner and you are ready to play the game!

SCOOBY'S

You buy Shaggy an ice cream, **take another turn**

Scooby sniffs out a BBQ at square 4. **Go back to check it out!**

Help Velma to write some postcards. **Miss a turn.**

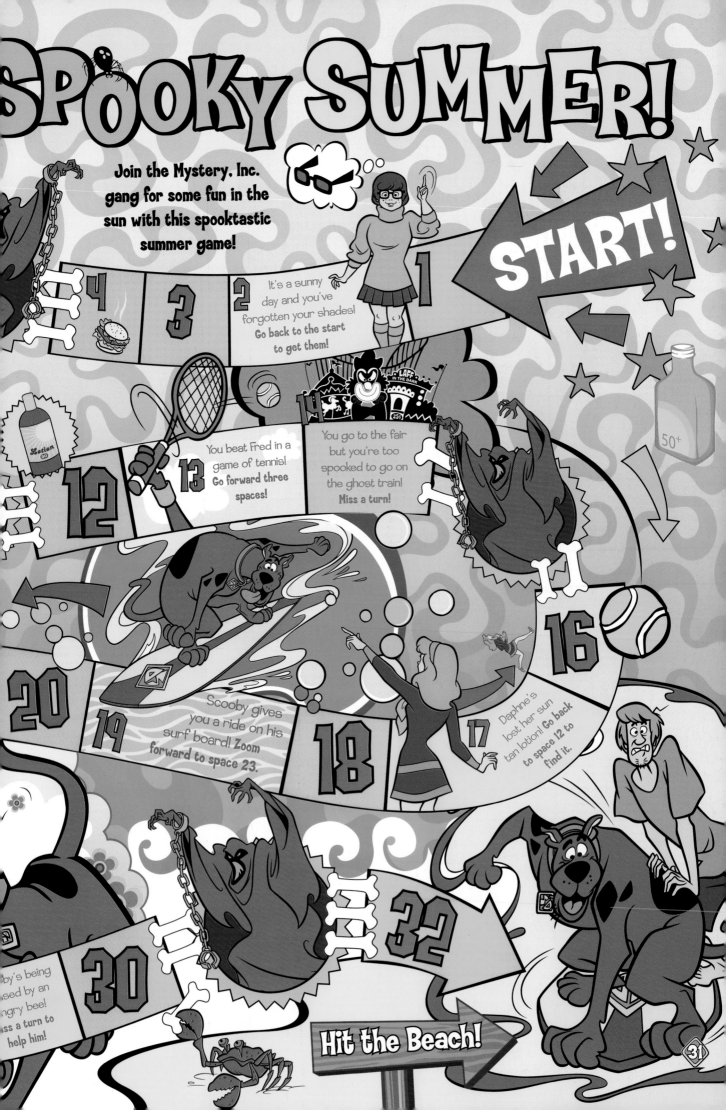

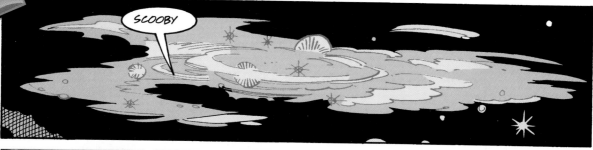

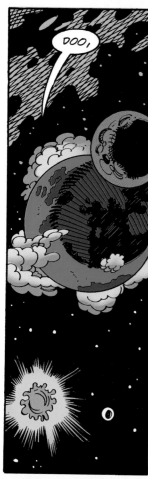

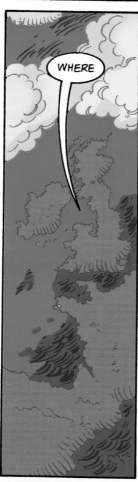

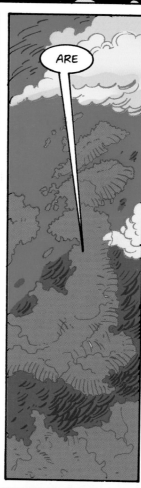

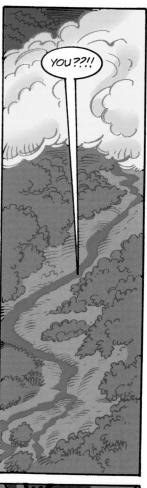

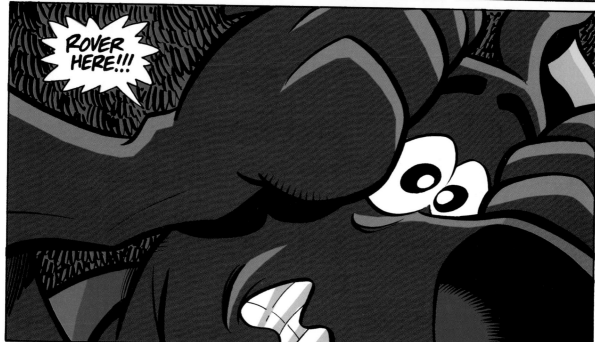

SCOOBY'S
AMAZE-ING
ADVENTURE

CHRIS DUFFY • WRITER
JOE STATON • PENCILS
ANDREW PEPOY • INKS
JOHN COSTANZA • LETTERS
RICK TAYLOR • COLORS
MIKE BRISBOIS • ASSISTANT EDITOR
BROWNWYN TAGGART • EDITOR

"...If you think back, you'll remember that we all agreed to tour the most mysterious sites of England on vacation.

"Velma and Fred were busy with school projects, so you two offered to escort me.

"After a couple of standard, ho-hum mysteries, we decided to unwind at Glenglogur, an old estate with a beautiful hedge maze open to the public.

Try the Maze at **Glenglogur**
IT'S FUN!
IT'S RELAXING!

"But when we got here, Clyde Yew, the caretaker, told us the maze was closed because some ghoul was haunting the maze!

CLOSED DUE TO HAUNTING!

"All the local inns were booked, so we were invited to stay over at the estate's manor by its owner, Lord Puffin.

"He told us that a legendary wood spirit, GLOGUR, was trying to drive people away from the area because the maze was built on the spirit's home!

"His creepy butler, Greaves, seemed to think the story was foolish."

POO-POO! NONSENSE!

THEN WE SPLIT UP TO LOOK FOR CLUES--TO SEE IF WE COULD PROVE GLOGUR WAS A FAKE!

WE REGROUPED WHEN IT GOT DARK, BUT SCOOBY HAD SOMEHOW WANDERED INTO THE MAZE AND GOTTEN LOST. WHICH BRINGS US UP TO NOW!

LIKE, WHEN I SAID "HOW'D WE GET INTO THIS," IT WAS JUST AN EXPRESSION.

HEE HEE HEE HEE! HA HAHAHA!

BEWARE, INTERLOPERS!

ZOINKS!

WHOMSOEVER I FIND IN YON LABYRINTH WILL SUFFER GREATLY!

HE'S PASSING US BY!

GOOD!

NOW THEN, WE'RE GOING TO NEED SOME--

--SCOOBY SNACKS? OH, NO!

LIKE, HE'S GOING INTO THE MAZE! WE'VE GOT TO HELP SCOOBY!

FLING

HOPE THIS WORKS!

YES!

HERE'S THE PLAN, SHAG: YOU RUN INTO THE MAZE, SAVE SCOOBY, AND CHASE GLOGUR BACK OUT. I'LL TRAP HIM AS HE EXITS!

SPLONK

LIKE, HAVE YOU FLIPPED? I CAN BARELY STAND UP, MY KNEES ARE KNOCKING SO HARD! HOW AM I GONNA GET BRAVE ENOUGH TO DO ALL THAT?

EASY! I JUST THREW OUR LAST SCOOBY SNACK ONTO THE BACK OF GLOGUR. AND THEY DON'T MAKE SCOOBY SNACKS IN EUROPE, SO THAT'S THE ONLY ONE LEFT ON THIS WHOLE CONTINENT!

CONTINUED ON PAGE 38

CREEPY CRAWLERS!

These giant critters will make you jump! They also have moving mandibles which are great for storing memos and notes.

YOU WILL NEED:

Three balloons, newspaper, PVA glue, cardboard tubes, thick card, corrugated card, scissors, pencil, sticky tape, paints and a paintbrush, mini clothes pegs

Change the oil in the Mystery Machine!

Remember to buy Snacks!

TO MAKE THE STAG BEETLE:

1 Draw an oval on thick card and cut it out. Screw up some newspaper and tape it to the middle of the oval.

2 Wrap three pieces of corrugated card over the top of the newspaper, taping them into place as you go.

These make the three sections of the beetle's body.

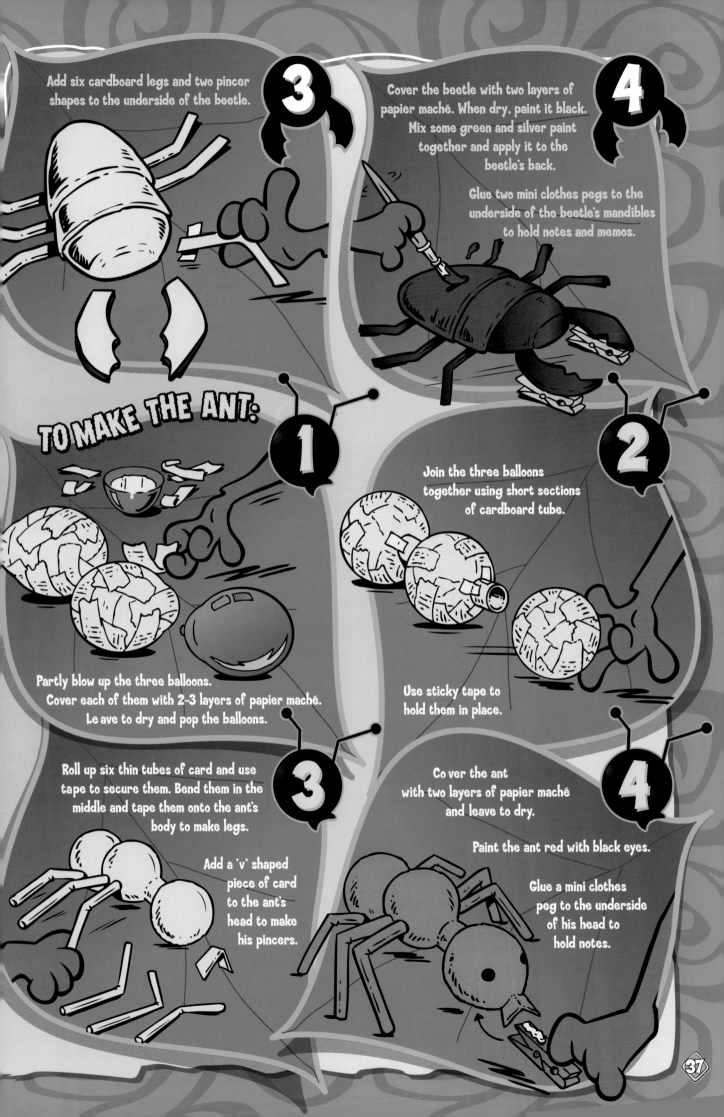

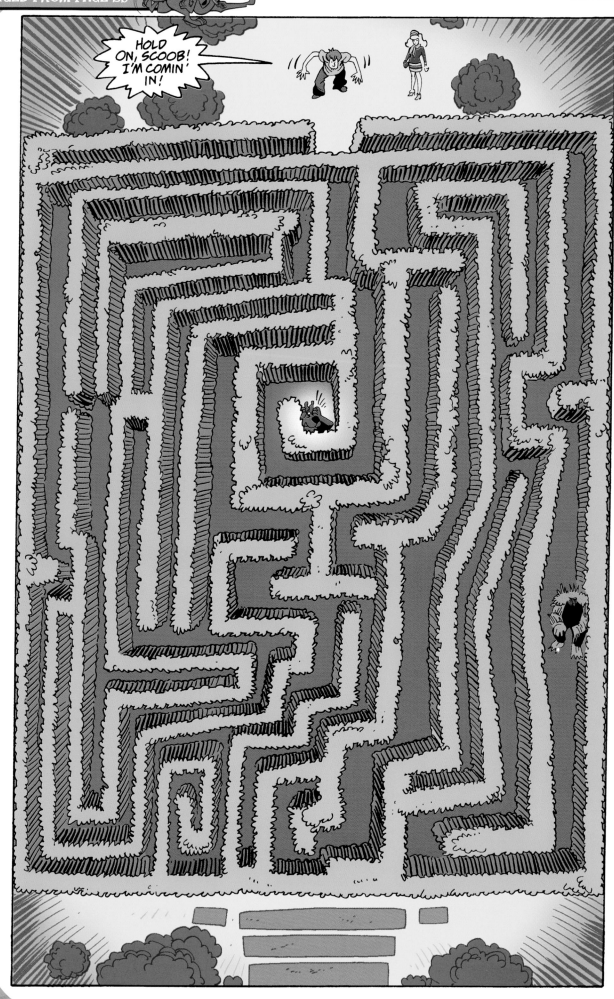

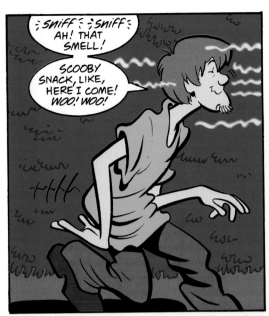

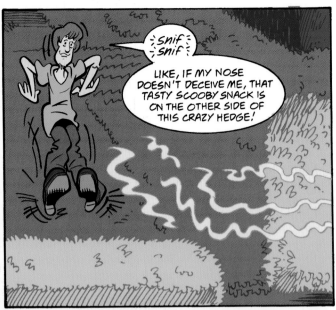

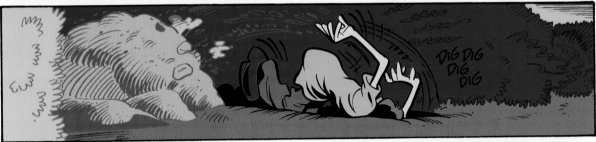

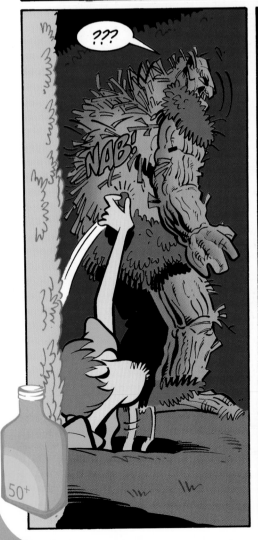

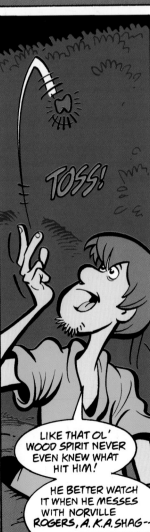

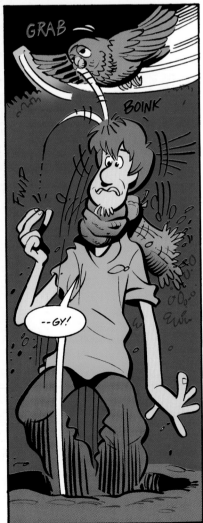

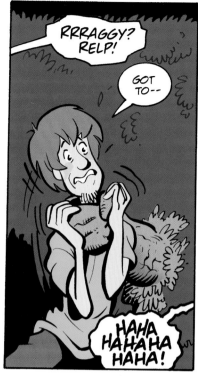

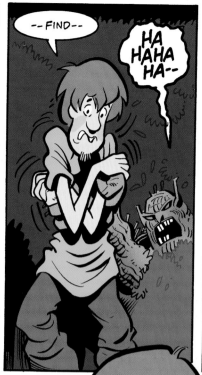

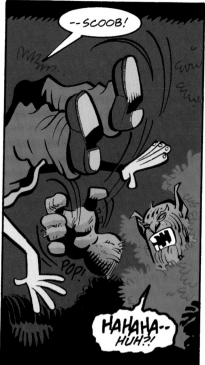

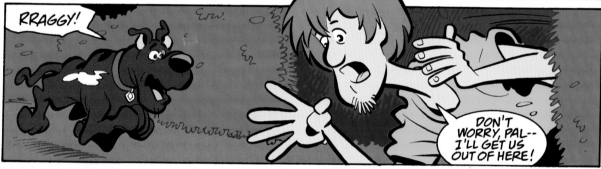

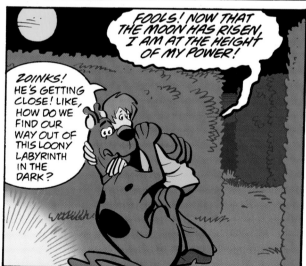

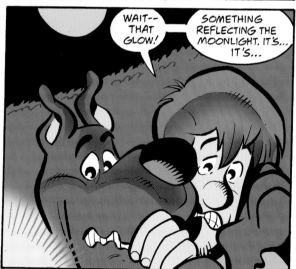

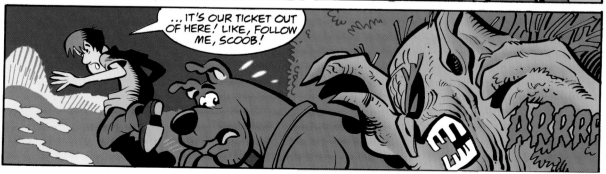

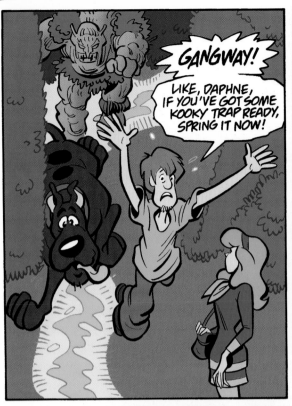

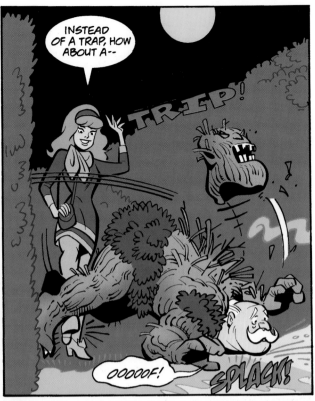

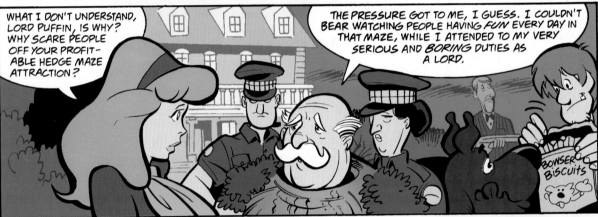

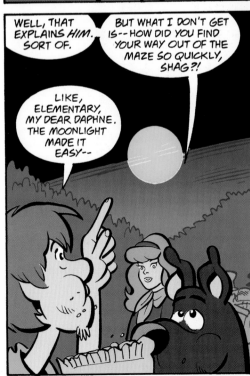

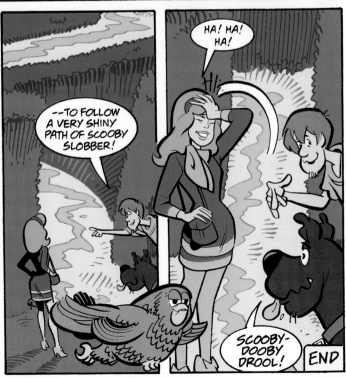

END

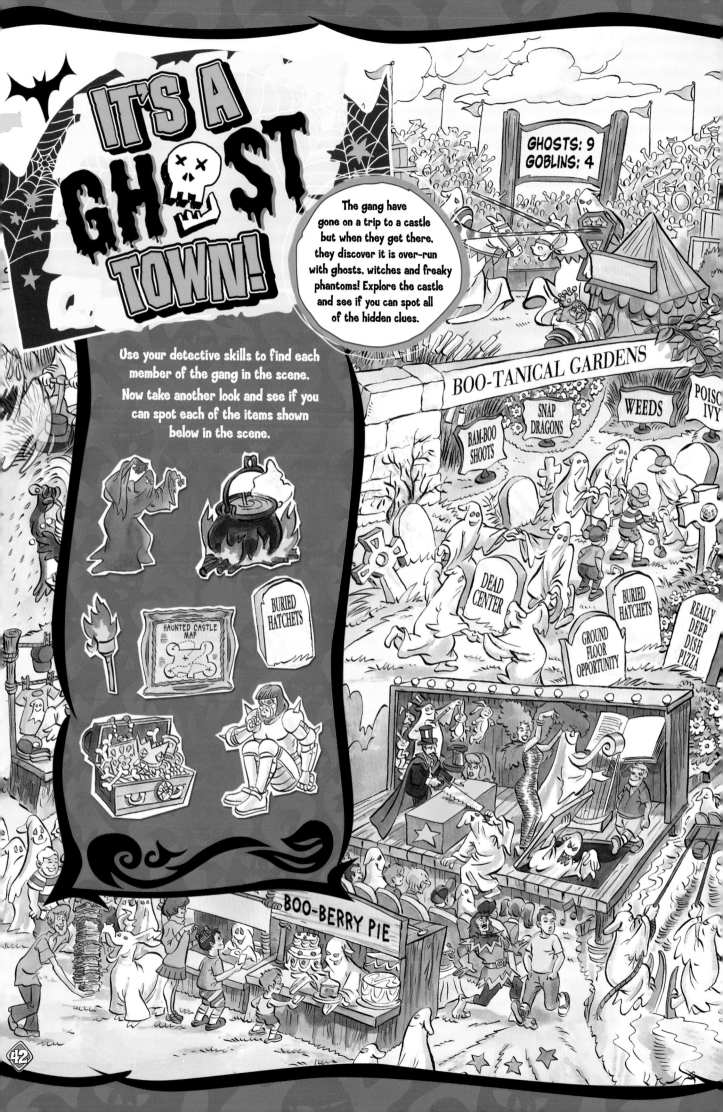

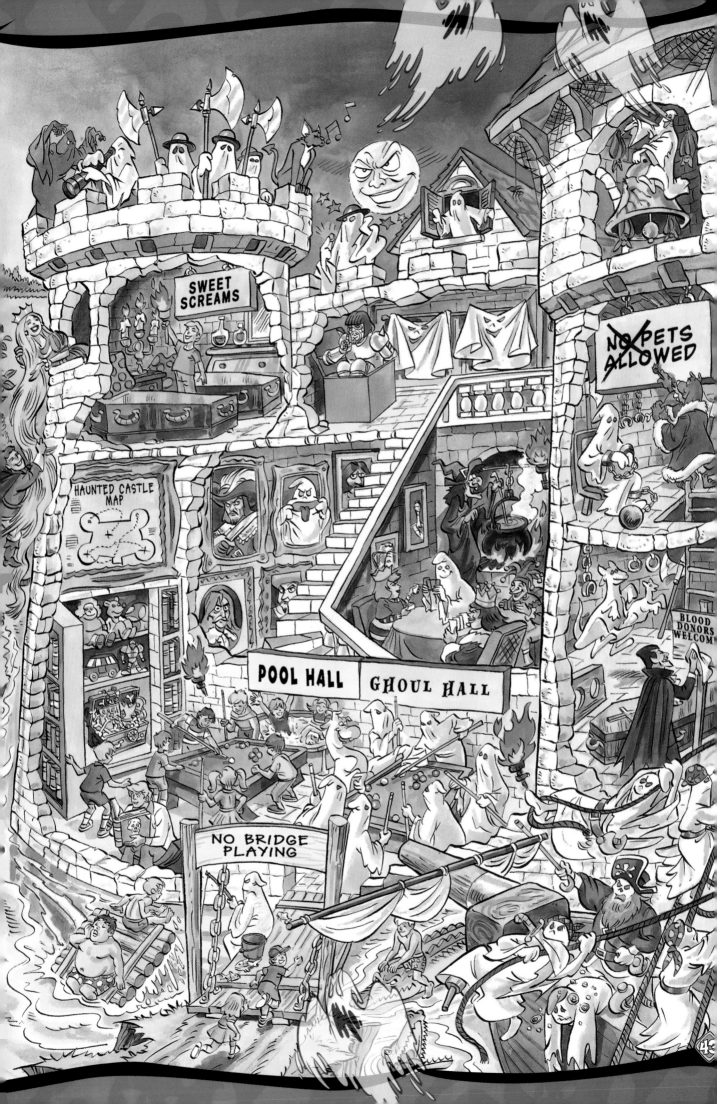

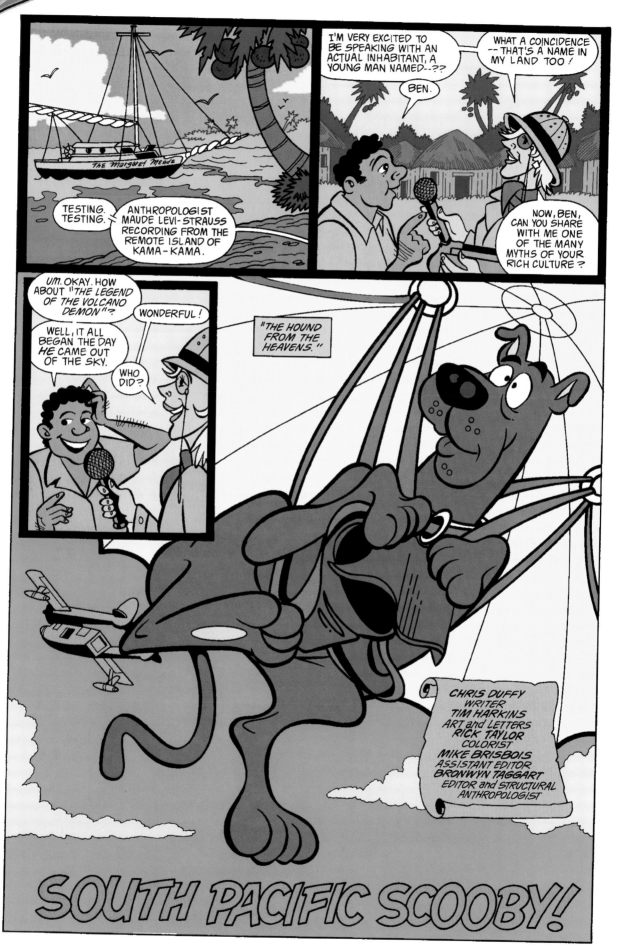

SOUTH PACIFIC SCOOBY!

THE ELDER GODS HAD SENT HIM TO US BECAUSE HE WAS THEIR BRAVEST WARRIOR.

HE'S OKAY! HE LANDED JUST OFF THE BEACH OF THAT ISLAND! HE CAN DOG-PADDLE TO SHORE.

POOR SCOOB. HE'S SCARED OF JUMPING OFF DIVING BOARDS, NEVER MIND AIRPLANES!

THE ELDER GODS ARE WISE INDEED.

YOU GOTTA, LIKE, TURN AROUND! THAT'S MY DOG DOWN THERE!

SORRY, GUY. CAN'T STOP-- I'M BRINGING IMPORTANT MEDICAL SUPPLIES TO SPAGO-SPAGO. WE CAN BE BACK FOR YOUR POOCH IN A WEEK!

BESIDES, YOU SHOULDN'T HAVE BEEN PLAYING WITH THAT PARACHUTE BY THE CARGO DOOR.

LIKE, SO HELP ME, I THOUGHT OUR FOOD WAS IN THAT BAG!

WHEN WE FIRST SAW HIM, THIS BRAVE BEAST WAS CHANTING POWERFUL MAGIC WORDS!

RAGGY! RAGGY!

YOU'VE COME!

WELCOME, MIGHTY ONE!

RIPES!

THE WARRIOR SEEMED EXCITED TO SEE US...

RELP!

RIPES!

... AND IMPRESSED BY THE HOLY IDOLS WE HAD BUILT FOR HIM.

OF COURSE, WE HAD TO GREET SUCH AN ESTEEMED VISITOR WITH A FEAST...

... AND A CELEBRATION.

AFTER WHICH, THE WARRIOR WAS VERY THOUGHTFUL.

ZZZZZZZ ZZ

SO IT SEEMED LIKE A GOOD TIME TO EXPLAIN THE LEGEND OF THE VOLCANO DEMON...

... HOW THE DEMON GUARDED THE RICH, FERTILE SOUTHERN HALF OF THE ISLAND...

... AND HOW, ON OUR HALF OF THE ISLAND, A TERRIBLE BLIGHT HAD DESTROYED OUR FRUIT TREES.

AND, OF COURSE, WE TOLD HIM --

-- HOW THE LEGEND FORETOLD OF A GREAT CONFLICT BETWEEN THE HOUND AND THE MONSTER.

CONTINUED ON PAGE 48

Paint a Picture!

Grab your pens and add some colour to this arty scene!

THAT NIGHT, THE HOUND FROM HEAVEN PRAISED THE GODS FOR GIVING HIM SUCH A WORTHY MISSION.

BUT THE NEXT MORNING, IT ALMOST SEEMED THE WARRIOR WAS RELUCTANT TO JOURNEY TO THE DEMON'S LAIR.

RELPPP!

WE SHOWED THE WARRIOR MANY PRECIOUS GOODS THE GODS HAD SENT US IN THE PAST.

PRODUCE

WE OFFERED THEM ALL TO HIM IN RETURN FOR HIS SERVICES. BUT THE HOUND WOULD HAVE NONE OF IT.

BUT FINALLY, SOMETHING CAUGHT HIS EYE.

SCOOBY SNACKS
SCOOBY SNACKS
SCOOBY SNACKS
SCOOBY SNACKS

AND WE WERE SHOWN THE FULL EXTENT OF THE WARRIOR'S AMAZING FLYING POWER!

SCOOBY SNACKS

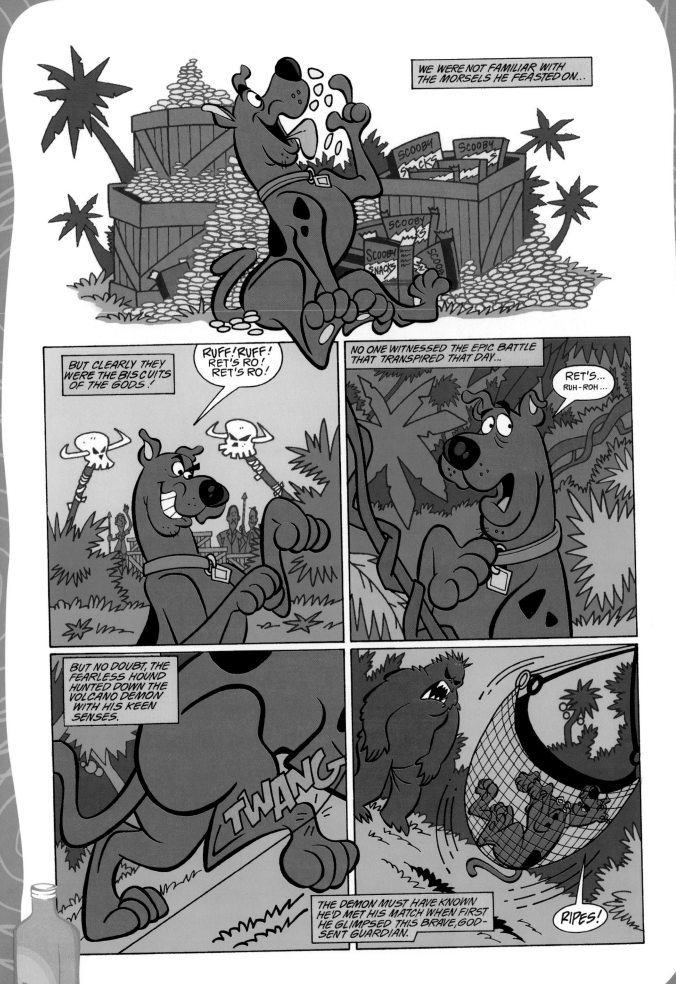

STILL, THE FIERCE COMBAT MUST HAVE TAKEN ALL THE HOUND'S CUNNING...

CRACK!

...SKILL...

...STEALTH...

...WISDOM...

RRRELLP!

RRRELLP!

...MAGIC WORDS OF POWER...

...GRACE...

...AND DIGNITY.

...IN THE END, THE DEMON WAS REVEALED AS A MERE MORTAL...

A MORTAL WHO HAD BEEN DRESSING AS THE VOLCANO DEMON TO KEEP THE LUSH, FERTILE HALF OF THE ISLAND TO HIMSELF.

WITH THE HOUND'S MISSION COMPLETED, THE ELDER GODS CAME TO TAKE HIM HOME.

ONE GOD, WITH A VISAGE AS BRISTLY AS A PINEAPPLE, SEEMED INTERESTED IN OUR TRIBUTE.

WHOAH--SCOOB, LIKE, HOW CAN I GET IN ON SOME OF THIS SNACKIN' ACTION?

SO WE THOUGHT HE MIGHT BE INTERESTED IN HELPING US WITH THE CRAB-DEMON THAT HAD BEEN SCARING PEOPLE AWAY FROM GOOD FISHING SPOTS.

BUT ALAS--

--THE PINEAPPLE GOD, IN HIS WISDOM, FELT IT WAS BEST THAT WE MORTALS DEALT WITH *THIS* MONSTER ON OUR OWN.

SO, THAT'S HOW THE VOLCANO DEMON WAS DEFEATED.

OH, THANK YOU, BEN. THAT WAS GREAT!

YOU'RE WELCOME!

THAT STORY WILL GET ME ANOTHER 10 YEARS' WORTH OF GRANT MONEY!

OH, MAUDE, YOU'VE DONE IT AGAIN!

WHAT'S UP, BEN?

NADA MUCHO. ANOTHER ANTHROPOLOGIST ON THE BEACH THIS MORNING.

YOU TELL 'EM WE THINK THE WORLD IS A BIG COCONUT FLOATING IN A MANGO JUICE OCEAN?

OR WAS IT THE ONE WHERE THE MOON IS A BIG HORSE SHOE CRAB, EATING ITS OWN TAIL?

NEITHER. THIS TIME I TALKED ABOUT THE TIME MYSTERY INC. CAME TO THE ISLAND. OF COURSE, I EMBELLISHED THE TALE *JUST* A LITTLE.

YOU'RE EVIL, BEN.

NAH, JUST HUNGRY. PASS THE SCOOBY SNACKS.

ROOBY ROO!

YEAH, ROOBY-ROOBY ROO!

END!

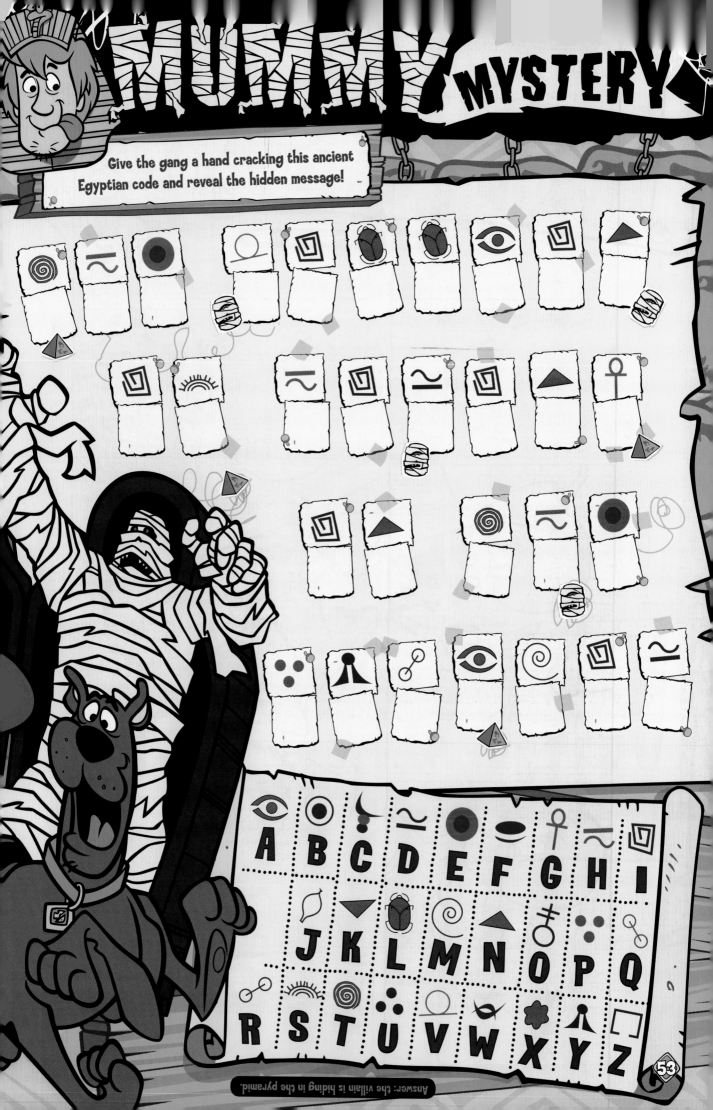

MUMMY MYSTERY

Give the gang a hand cracking this ancient Egyptian code and reveal the hidden message!

53

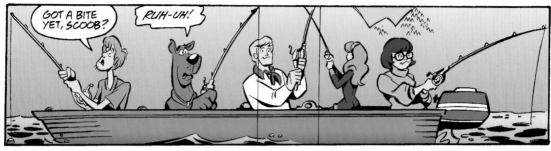

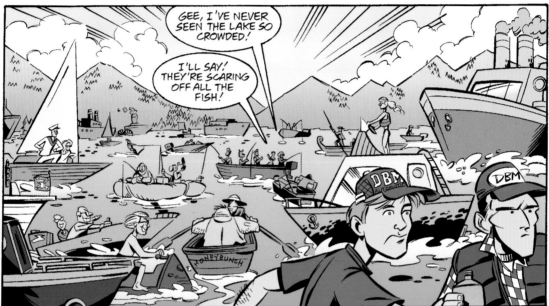

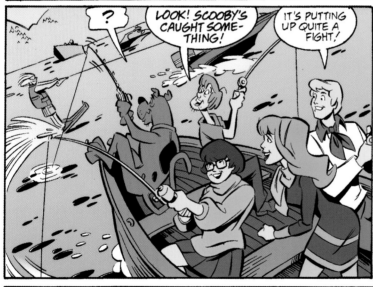

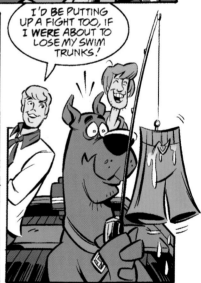

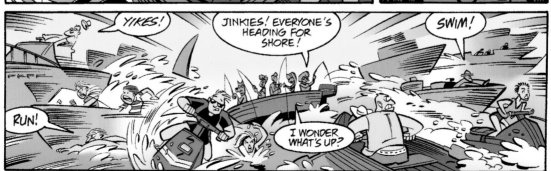

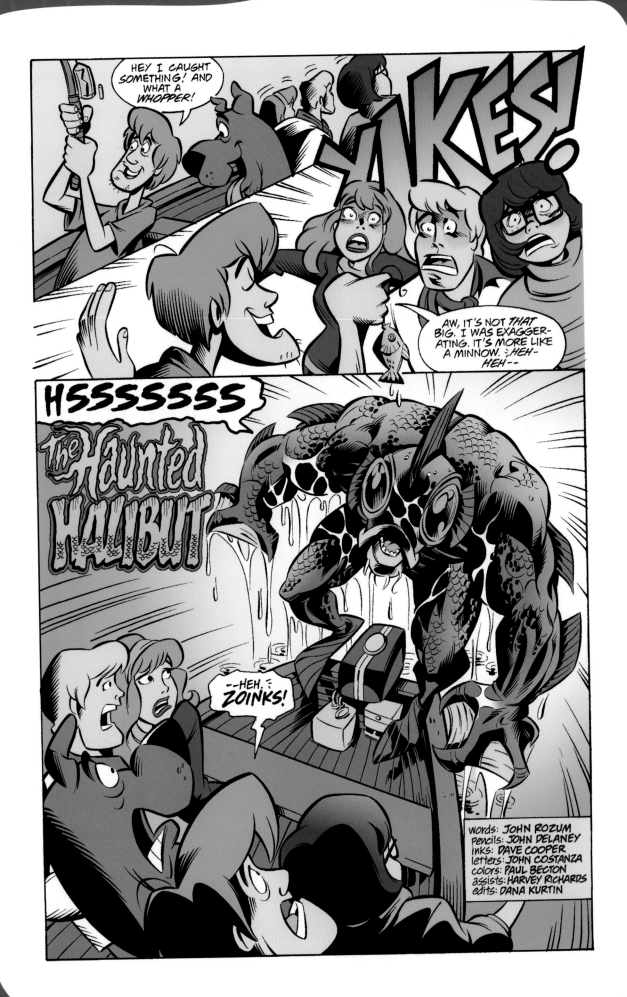

WHAT WAS THAT?!

I DON'T KNOW, AND I DON'T WANT TO KNOW. LET'S GET OUT OF HERE!

SPLASH

REAH, REAH! ROUT ROF RERE!

GOOD IDEA!

THAT WAS THE MAN-FISH OF HALIBUT LAKE! HE'S BEEN SCARING OFF ALL THE VACATIONERS!

RANGER RANGER

MAYBE WE COULD HELP.

YES! WE HAVE LOTS OF EXPERIENCE WITH MYSTERIES!

THANKS, KIDS, BUT WE ALREADY HAVE SOME-ONE!

DON'T YOU KIDS WORRY. BY THE TIME I'M DONE WITH THE MAN-FISH, HE'LL BE FIT FOR BATTER FRYING AND SOME TARTAR SAUCE!

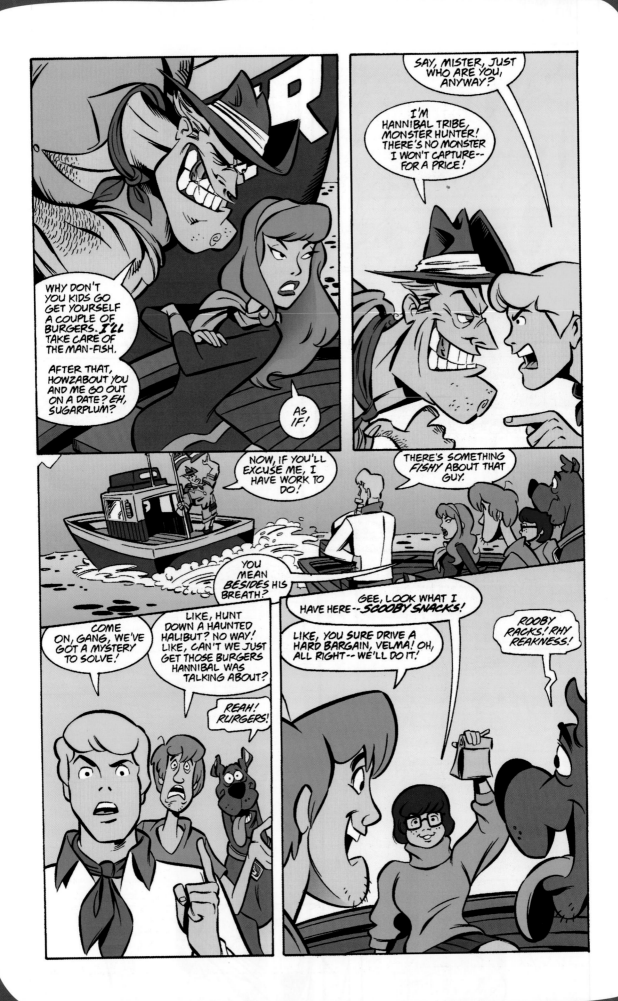

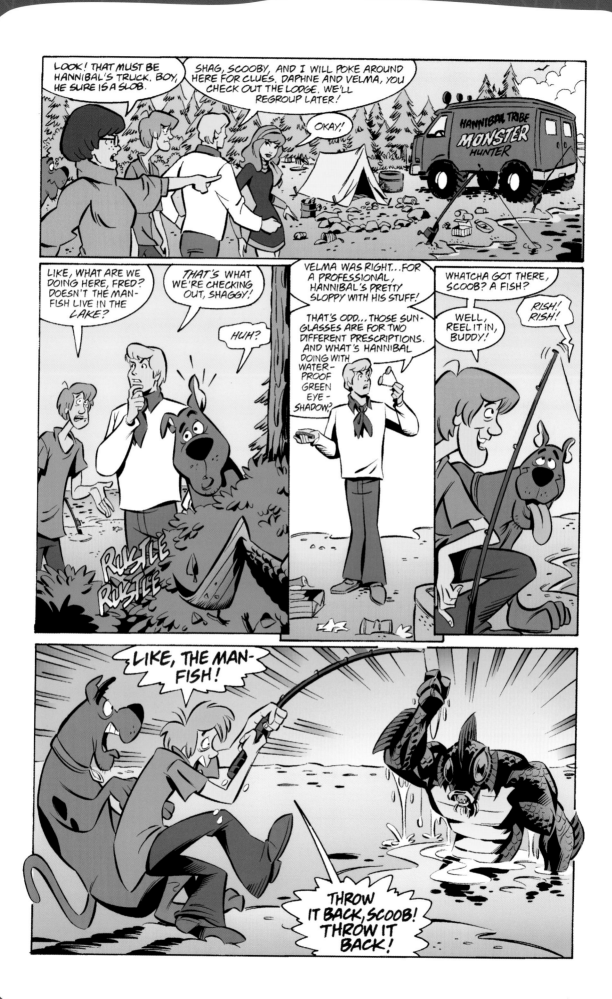

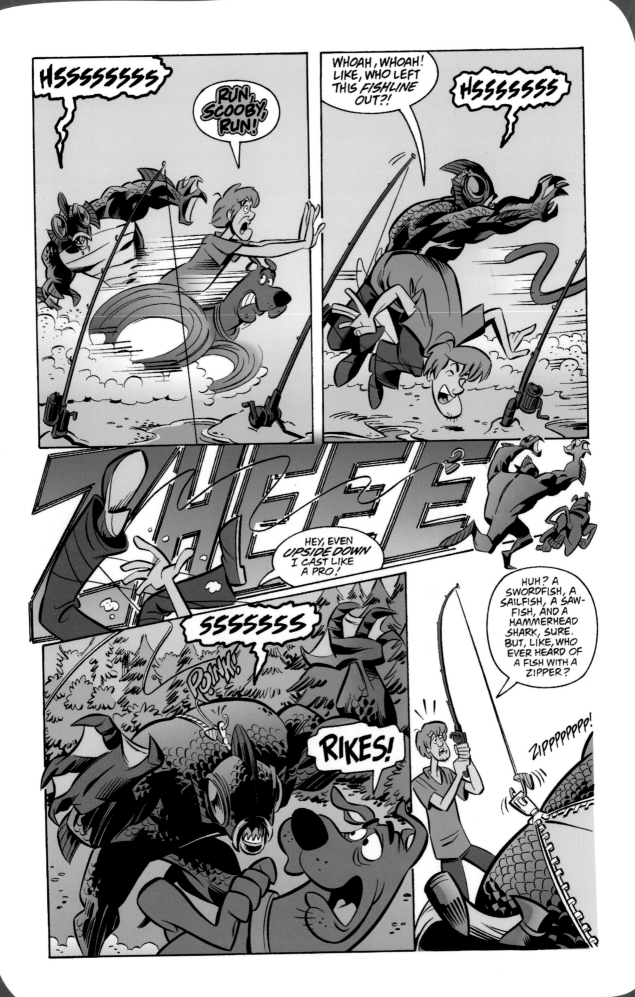

59

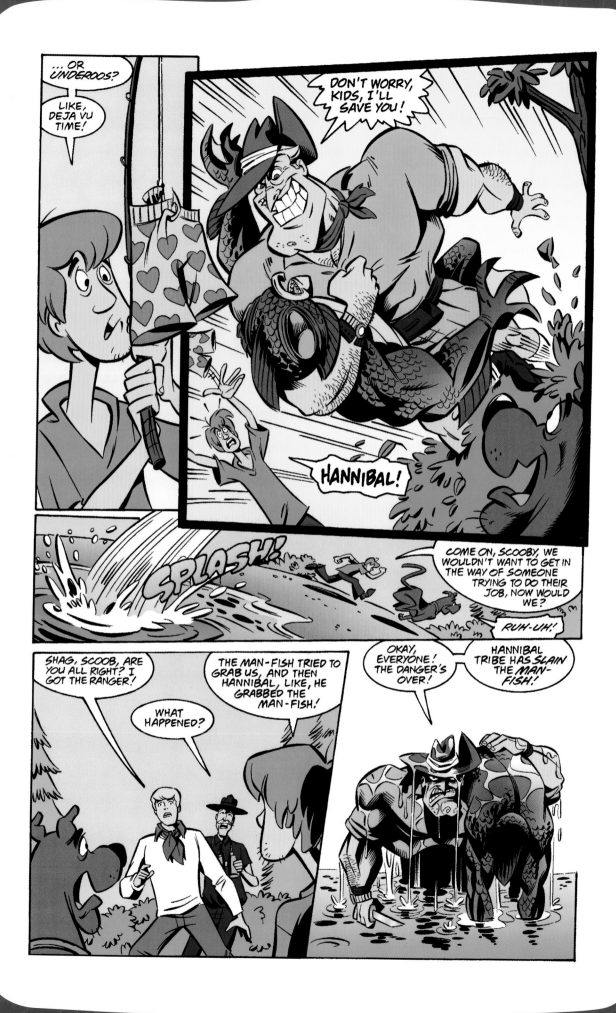

We called all of Hannibal's so-called ex-clients from the lodge. He's nothing but a scam artist!

He and his partner travel the world pretending to be a monster and a monster hunter. First they cause the problem, then they charge to solve it!

That explains the two sunglass prescriptions--and all the waterproof makeup! Hannibal and his buddy invented the man-fish from the beginning!

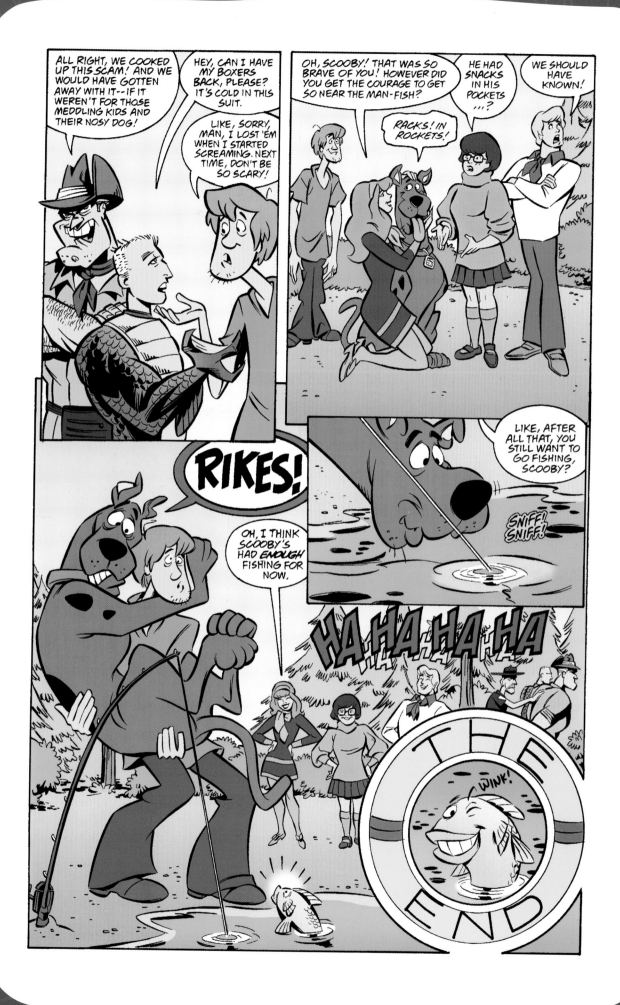

Velma's Detective Test!

Good detectives are always paying attention super sleuths! Were you paying attention during The Haunted Halibut comic strip?

Tick the correct answers! ✓

1
Where did the mystery take place?

 A

 B

 C

2
Can you spot something we've changed about the monster?

A Hair

B Eyes

C Tongue

3
What did Scooby catch here?

A

B

C

4
What word is blurred from the van below?

A Gorilla

B Monster

C Treasure

5
Who was behind the monster scam?

A

B

C Both

ANSWERS: 1) A, 2) C, 3) B, 4) B, 5) C.

63

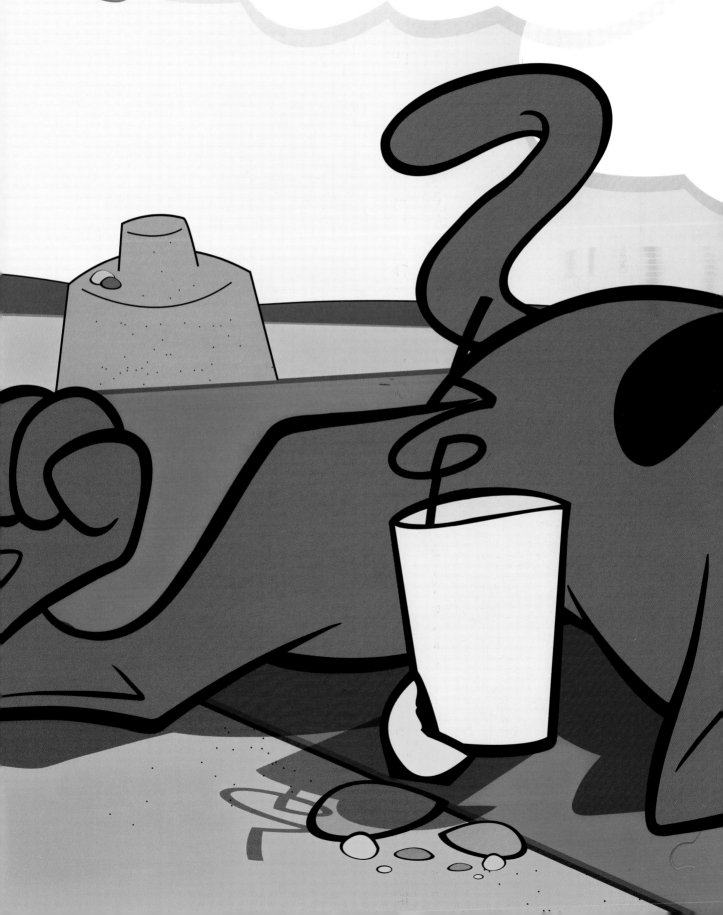

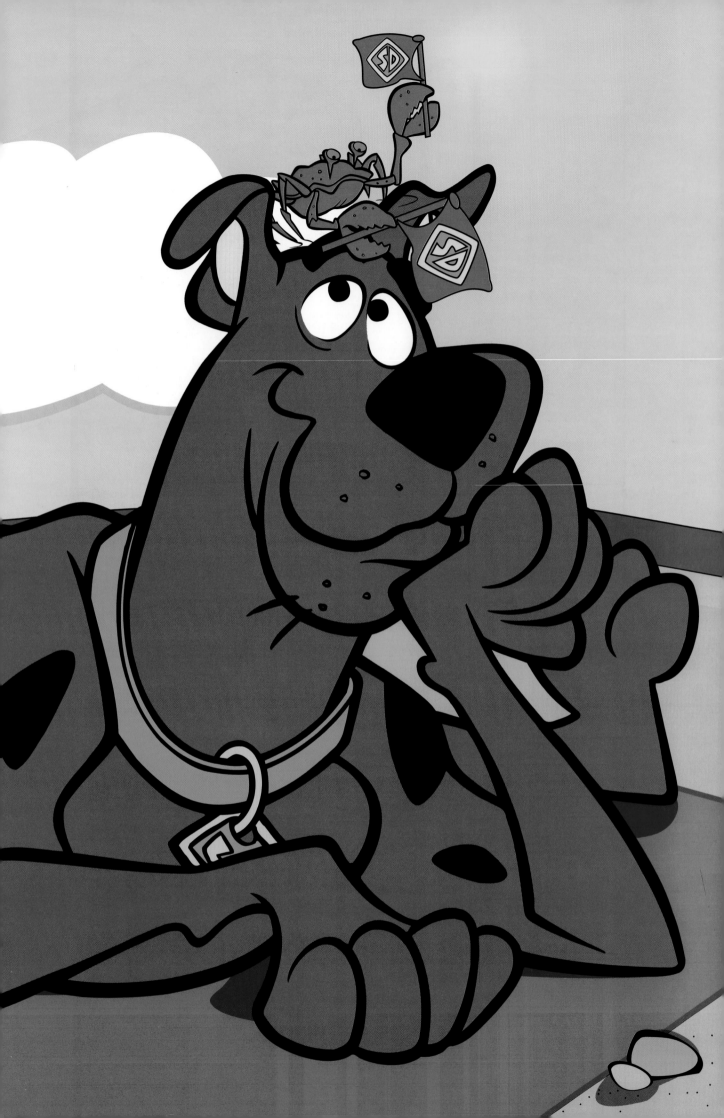

SUMMER ANNUAL

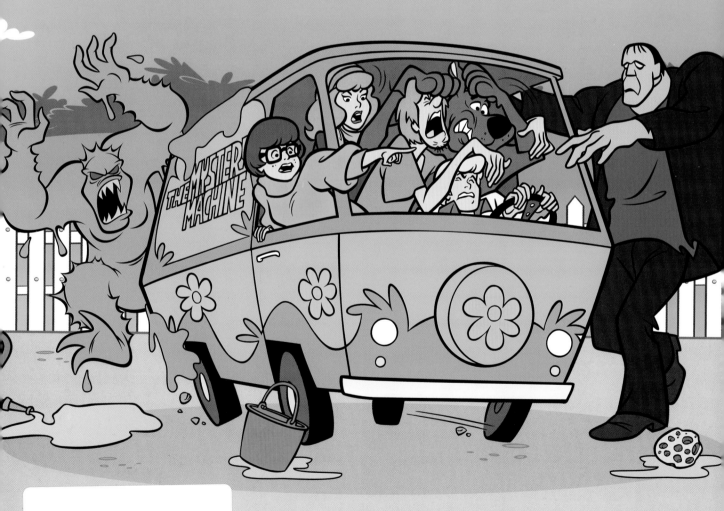